Bridge Is A Funny Game

by

Mikhael Kollander

and

Gerry Fox

FOREWORD

What do you do with a son-in-law who is a talented cartoonist but doesn't play bridge? Well, when you discover a common bond with puns and jokes, obviously, you do a book together. Since one of us can't even draw a straight line and the other can scarcely shuffle a deck of cards, it was a natural collaboration.

So, what makes bridge such a funny game? It's all about the people who play at it. In these cartoons we have tried to capture the spirit, the mood, the demeanor – that is, the humor, intentional or not – that players bring to the table. Be they duffers or pros, it is their actions and reactions that create such fertile ground for comical situations.

If you, dear reader, can recognize some of your partners and opponents in these cartoons, do not be surprised. You might even recognize yourself. In any event, we hope you enjoy them at least as much as we enjoyed creating them.

Our wives, Janice Kollander and Barbara Fox, deserve special acknowledgement for their contribution to this book. As guinea pigs for each new cartoon, the volume of their laughter (or lack thereof) helped us to judge the worthiness of each one. Without their "editorial" assistance this book would have been much larger and decidedly less funny.

Mikhael Kollander and Gerry Fox

Honey, it's your mother on the phone. She's desperate for a fourth. Are you free to play?

Really, Horton, when I asked you to be my partner,
a simple NO would have been sufficient...

Abdullah, must you do that **every** time you take a trick?

I have an uneasy feeling about this pair..

Any time, Carruthers, any time...

Why should we let you in? You reneged six times last year, twice you passed a forcing bid, and you didn't attempt a single slam.

Of course, the guy called you a fish.
Your bidding and play can sure stink
up a game.

Watch out for these two. They play
an unusual big club system...

A fourth, a fourth. My kingdom for a fourth...

Stop bugging me with your bridge problems...

Cancer, schmantzer! The game starts at 7:30.
Are you going to be there or not?

We have to let him play. He's the fastest dealer
in the club..

You can kiss my asp. I'm tired of your griping about my bidding...

Perhaps it was imprudent for Williams to double the Captain...

Some come for the game. Jenkins comes for the food. His partner knows better than to show up on time...

Look, for now, all we can play is poker!
The bridge game will have to wait until
we get more people!

BEE HUMOR

Did you hear the latest buzz about the Queen?
She took up bridge, but her game simply had
no sting to it.

Well, Hastings, I see you are prepared to be
more competitive tonight.

Regardless of your initial impression of me,
you'll find me an erudite and engaging player.
Do you have any bananas?

Bridge tonight. My igloo at sunset...

Melvin, wake up! I finally figured out how to
make that 4S doubled contract..

How was I to know you wanted a spade?
I was just making a blind lead...

Mona's not a great player, but
she's the ideal kibbbitzer..

Hold on just a minute! How do you know I have
six hearts and seventeen points? We haven't
started the auction yet...!

Farmer John's in a bad mood. He lost big at bridge last night and made me do grunt work all morning.

We didn't abduct you to reproduce with your species. We just need a fourth...

No, dear. The men aren't fighting. They're just playing bridge...

You're bidding without any guts this evening...

Perhaps I'm being paranoid, but my dummy play
has suffered of late...

You're late again...

Pay no attention. They don't know
what they're talking about...

Okay, one more time....One trumpet calls for a
club lead, two for a diamond, three for a heart, and
a full water spray demands a spade....

I told Father Moynihan just this morning that
his sermons are much too long....

Houston, we have a problem. The two Russian astronauts do not play bridge. Please send replacements ASAP....

(Lest there be any doubt as to the origins of the game...)

Looks like you made a fatal mistake
with that last bid...

I'm guessing that this is your first exposure
to the game..

Perhaps my partner and I should just let him
make his contract...

Still working on the riffle, Simonson...?

Honestly, Otto. why did you get in the lotus
position right before the game? You'll never
get yourself unstuck in time for the first hand.

Yes, I know you are playing Goren, It's the Taoist version your partner is using that I don't understand.

Griselda constantly complains about Horton's game, but nothing seems to bother him...

Forgive me, for I have sinned. Today, I miscounted trumps twice, I called out of turn, and I made three insufficient bids...

For the last time, Cheryl, you've got to stop that clucking whenever you think you've done something good at the bridge table...

Enlightened or not, your bidding still stinks...

Enough already, Felix...It's your turn to bid.
Do you really have to groom yourself after every hand?

I know we were desperate for a fourth, but, if he prefaces one more bid with, "This little piggy went to market...," I'm going to butcher him on the spot.

I see your partner is acquainted with
the holdup play...

Sally, you check the train station. Harry, you
try the bus depot. I'll start knocking on doors.
There has to be another bridge player in this
backwater place.

Of course, I shot my husband. After all, he
went down in an ice-cold grand slam...

I think we bought an entry for the wrong event...

Four score and seven plays ago, you revoked
and trumped my winning trick...

I can't handle playing bridge with you any more...
but, I still want to be your significant otter.

I know I advised you to put more teeth
into your bidding, Friedman. Your sarcasm is
duly noted.

Maybe, we should just start using conventional signals. I don't
know about you, but the accordian is getting heavy...

Actually, I prefer bridge to poker. The game
moves much more slowly...

Hey, pal. We're waiting for you to bid.
Meditate on your own time!

The bad news is that he wants to kill us all.
The good news is that he plays bridge...

Bridge? You've got to be kidding.
I don't think they're smart enough
to play Go Fish...

Ever since Jenkins made that grand slam, he's been
beside himself...

I know it looks gross, but it's won me
a lot of tournaments over the years...

My goodness. I got dealt a perfect bust....

Make it a double, Joe. My bridge partner
has left me for a younger player

It's customary to invite Yamada San to cut the cards....

Here comes that bridge player again.
He has this kinky idea about quick tricks.

Your bidding always makes scents to me...

His bidding leaves a lot to be desired, but he plays the cards like a magician.

No, the poor man's not sea sick. His partner
just trumped his ace...

Wiser? You think bridge makes you wiser?
Frankly, Oscar, I don't give a hoot for the game.

Forget about it. They're bridge players....way too tough.

Blast it, Marcel. When the club voted for
silent auctions, we were thinking about
bidding boxes, not hand signals.

Iv'e decided to let the chips fall
where they may, except at the
bridge table, of course...

The Seal of Approval

Honestly, all you want to do is play bridge and spawn.
Bridge and spawn! Bridge and spawn! Really, Frank,
I do need some time to myself!

Yes, it actually was good for me too, until I remembered you
doubling me in four spades last night.

I do realize that you're sensitive to criticism, Al,
but if you want to be a tournament player,
you'll just have to develop a thicker skin...

My gastroenterologist was my bridge partner.
We came in last at the club yesterday...
Now he hates my guts.

This pair is inscrutable. Don't even try
to figure out what they are doing...

For God's sake, man! Breast your cards!

Look! I'm not E.F. Hutton. I'm not Charles Goren.
I'm playing bridge online, and I can't stand kibitzers.

Why do I get the feeling that we're
about to be squeezed?

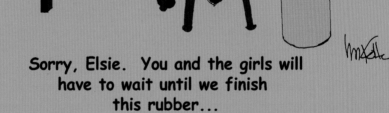

Sorry, Elsie. You and the girls will
have to wait until we finish
this rubber...

Idiot! You kidnapped the wrong hostage. This one doesn't play bridge..

Come on, Fayed. Don't be a sore loser.
It's only a game...

I tried to learn how to play bridge once, but for the life of me, I just couldn't figure out how to hold the cards.

Jenkins used to be a tile setter. Be patient......

I don't understand why I keep getting fleeced
at online bridge...

But, sweetheart, that was only our first game as partners. I'm sure we'll do better next time.

Who would have thought the penalty for being
a hand hog would be so severe?

I hear the guy in the red trunks is an excellent bidder.
Let's try him first. Maybe, that will help your game..

If my human wins at bridge tonight, I get
extra kibbles.   If she looses, all I get
is a bunch of hard luck stories.

You fool! This is a nonsmoking club..!

Yes, I know we're halfway to South America,
but how often do we get invited to one of
Mrs. Throckmorton's bridge parties?
Shall we turn around and go back?

I am seeking
enlightenment

I've chosen chastity,
a vegetarian diet, and
no more material posessions.

I might even give up bridge.

My thoughts are purer now.

I can live without sex,
meat, and my iPhone.

But I'd kill for a terrific partner
at the Friday night game.

Playing the sympathy card, Hoskins...?

If he starts huffing and puffing, grab your cards
and get under the table..!

There goes the Thursday night game...

Do you mind if we play East-West?
We need the exercise...

If you weren't such a chicken, we
would have won big tonight!

With them it's a fast paced game. After every hand, however,
they disapear into the bushes for a minute or two...BUT,
they always come back with smiles on their faces.....

Give me a break! I'm only an amoeba. My partner
will be here shortly, just as soon as I
can reproduce myself...

At this rate it'll take a month just to complete
the first rubber...

Yes, Billy, I know Mommy just said a very bad word,
but Daddy just made a very stupid bid...

Our bridge teacher told us that eating people is good for the brain. We'll both have the catch of the day, but please remove the bones. And, make it snappy, or we'll be late for tonight's class.

I can't believe you forgot the cards....